BASTIEN PIANO BASICS
SUPPLEMENTARY

BASTIEN PLAY-ALONG
Classics

Jane Smisor Bastien, Lisa Bastien, & Lori Bastien

Preface

Bastien Play-Along Classics Book 1 is a collection of familiar excerpts from pieces by the master composers designed for beginning piano students. These elementary arrangements are complete with an Accompaniment Compact Disc. We hope this book and CD will be motivating and inspiring!

Sincerely,
Jane Smisor Bastien, Lisa Bastien, and Lori Bastien

You will see these icons above each new piece in this book. The circled numbers inside the icons indicate which track should be used with each piece. The metronome number at which the accompaniment has been recorded is shown under the track number. The compact disc can be found inside the back cover, and more information about the CD may be found on page 2.

ISBN 0-8497-7313-X

©2003 Kjos Music Press, 4380 Jutland Drive, San Diego, California 92117.
International copyright secured. All rights reserved. Printed in U.S.A.
Music ©1999, 2000 Kjos Music Press.
Warning! These arrangements are protected by copyright law.
To copy or reproduce them by any method is an infringement of the copyright law.
Anyone who reproduces copyrighted matter is subject to substantial penalties and assessments for each infringement.

About the *Accompaniment Compact Disc*

The CD for this book can be found attached inside the back cover of the book. The *Bastien Play-Along Classics Accompaniment Compact Disc* was created to musically enhance student practice sessions and improve understanding of phrasing, balance, rhythm, and pulse. Each piece in *Bastien Play-Along Classics* includes one CD track, recorded at a moderate practice tempo. The tempos allow students to use the accompaniments **as they learn** each piece, rather than waiting until the particular challenges of a piece have been mastered.

Each piece on the *Accompaniment Compact Disc* is preceded by a two measure count-off. On the first beat of each count-off measure, a metallic triangle "ding" is heard, followed by wooden stick "clicks" on the remaining beats of the measure. Once the music begins, tempo will vary as dictated by the markings in the music, such as a *ritardando*.

On each piece, background accompaniment instruments are heard on the left channel of the recording. The student piano part as it appears in the book is demonstrated on the right channel. On many sound systems, balance between the left and right channels may be changed, either by adjusting a single "left/right balance control," or by adjusting the volume of the left and right speakers individually. These adjustments allow isolation of either the accompaniment instruments or the student piano part, or modification of the blend between the two.

When first learning a piece, it is recommended that students adjust their sound systems so that the left and right channels are equal, or so that the right channel is favored, allowing the student piano part to be heard as clearly as possible. As students become more proficient playing a piece, it is suggested that they try adjusting their systems to favor the left channel, thus making the student piano part on the right channel very soft or completely silent. This will allow students to play the piano over the accompaniment without the added sound of the demonstration piano coming from the CD.

 If using an electronic keyboard, it is important that the pitch of the keyboard match the tuning note found on track 1 of the CD. This tuning note is A above middle C. The reference manual of each particular keyboard should provide information on how to make tuning adjustments.

Contents

✓

As students complete each piece, they may track their progress by checking (✓) off each title.

ODE TO JOY

Ludwig van Beethoven

BRIDAL MARCH

Richard Wagner

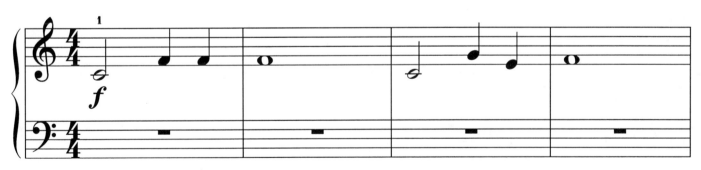

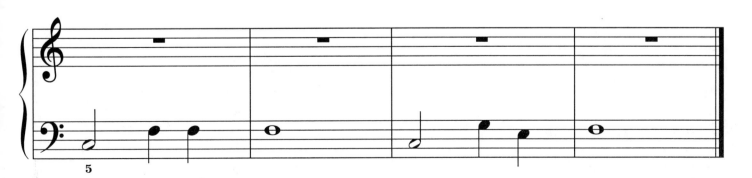

CAN CAN

from the opera
Orpheus in the Underworld

Jacques Offenbach

KP13

FANTAISIE IMPROMPTU

Frédéric Chopin

MINUET IN G

Johann Sebastian Bach

SURPRISE SYMPHONY

Franz Joseph Haydn

MUSETTE

Johann Sebastian Bach

THEME FROM SYMPHONY NO. 5

Peter Ilyich Tchaikovsky

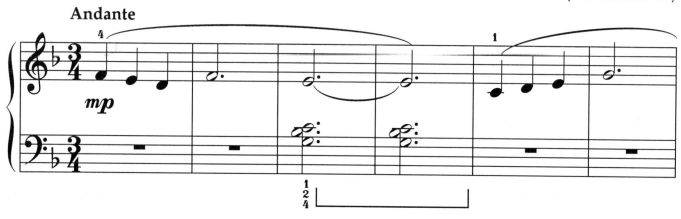

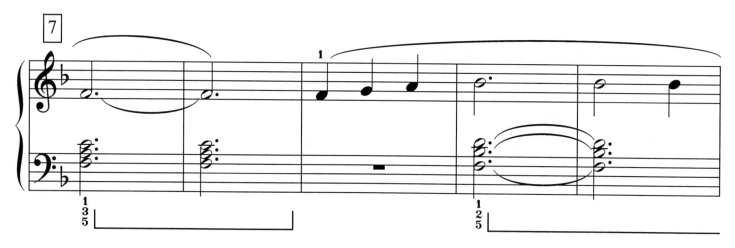

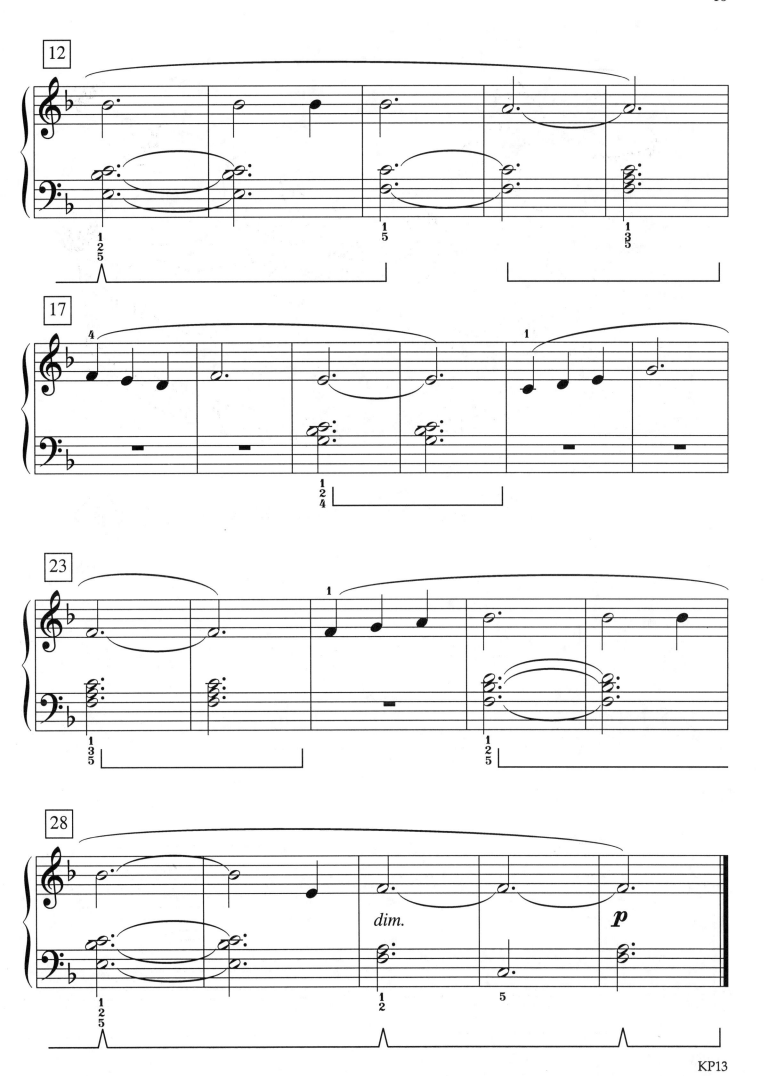

SPRING

from *The Four Seasons*

Antonio Vivaldi

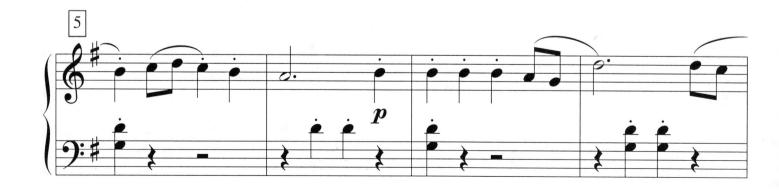

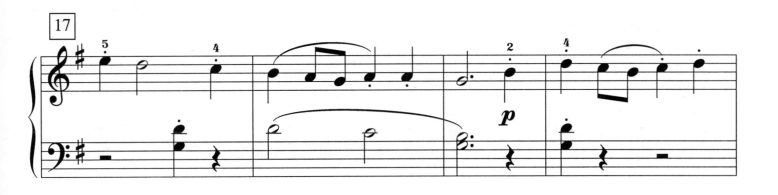

THE BLUE DANUBE WALTZ

Johann Strauss, Jr.

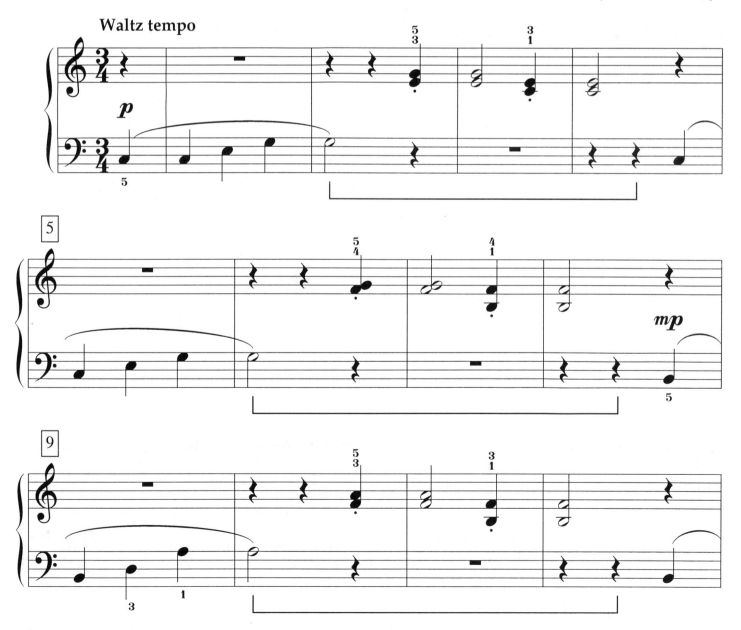

LAUGHING SONG
from the operetta *Die Fledermaus*

Johann Strauss, Jr.

SONATA THEME

from *Sonata in A Major, K. 331*

Wolfgang Amadeus Mozart

JESU, JOY OF MAN'S DESIRING

from *Cantata No. 147*

Johann Sebastian Bach

HALLELUJAH CHORUS

from the oratorio *Messiah*

George Frideric Handel

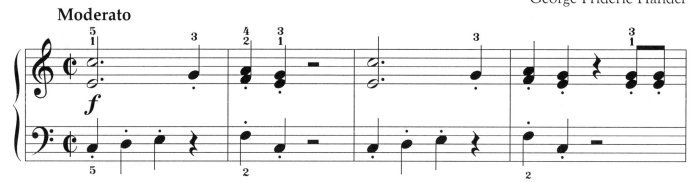

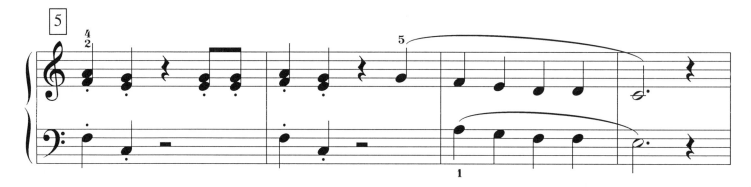

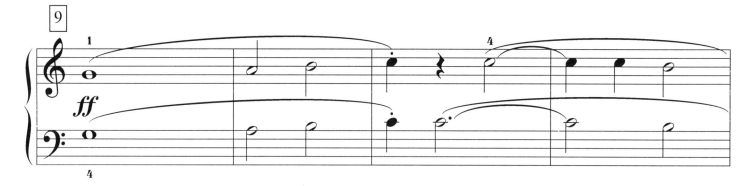

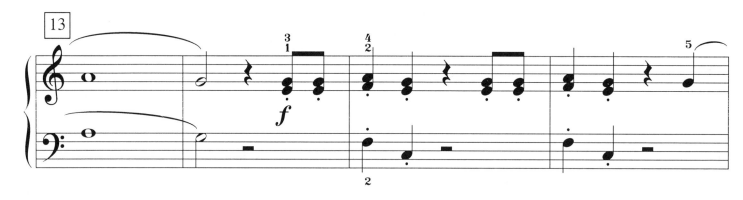

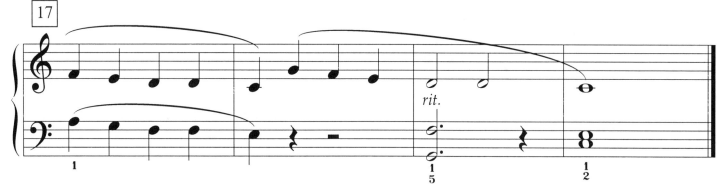